Contents

How to grow a seed

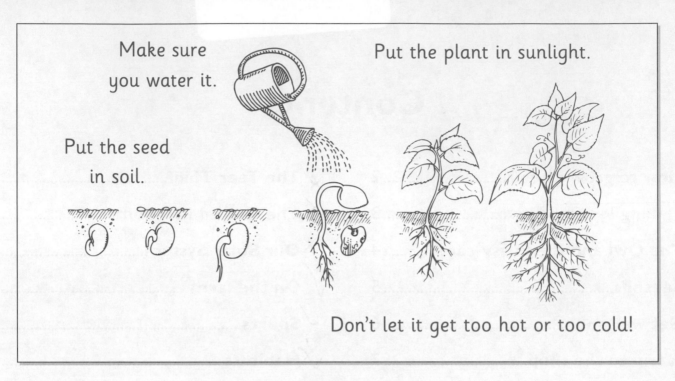

Make sure you water it.

Put the plant in sunlight.

Put the seed in soil.

Don't let it get too hot or too cold!

Put a circle around the correct answer.

1 Plants grow in... (soil) sugar salt

2 Place the plant somewhere... dark (sunny) cold

Write 'true' or 'false' for each sentence.

3 A plant grows into a seed. _true_

4 Seeds need water to grow. _true_

5 A seed grows best if it is very hot. _true_

Did you answer all the questions?

Making lemonade

Lemonade Recipe

You will need: 3 lemons, 100g sugar and 1 litre of water.

How to make:

- Squeeze the lemons so the juice goes into a large jug.

- Add the sugar to the lemon juice.

- Pour the water into the jug and stir until everything is mixed together.

- Add some ice cubes and enjoy your lemonade!

1 What is a "recipe"?

Squeeze lemons. Add sugar, Pour water, Mix together. Add ice cubes.

2 How many lemons do you need for this recipe?

3 lemons.

3 Write the number 1, 2, 3, 4 or 5 next to each sentence to show the right order. The first one has been done for you.

| 2 | Add the sugar. | 5 | Add some ice. | 3 | Add the water. |

| 4 | Mix it together. | | | 1 | Squeeze the lemons into a jug. |

Did you answer all the questions?

The Owl and the Pussy-cat

The Owl and the Pussy-cat went to sea

In a beautiful pea green boat,

They took some honey, and plenty of money,

Wrapped up in a five pound note.

The Owl looked up to the stars above,

And sang to a small guitar,

'O lovely Pussy! O Pussy my love,

What a beautiful Pussy you are,

You are,

You are!

What a beautiful Pussy you are!'

by Edward Lear

1 Name two things the owl and the cat took with them.

…Some honey… and …Plenty of money…

2 Which word in the poem rhymes with "above"?

…Star…

3 The boat was "pea green". Why is this a good way to describe a colour?

…Due to owl colour is green and even…
…sea colour is also green…

Did you answer all the questions?

Seasons

Spring

The weather starts to get warmer and flowers start to bloom. Lambs are born in the fields.

Summer

It is hotter. The trees have full green leaves. The days are longer and there are more insects.

Autumn

It starts to get colder. The leaves change colour and start to fall from the trees.

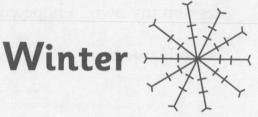
Winter

It is cold and sometimes it snows. Some animals sleep until spring. This is called hibernation.

1 In which season do trees start to lose their leaves?

Autumn

2 What does the word "hibernation" mean?

Some animals sleep until spring

3 Which is your favourite season? Why?

My favourite season is spring because the flowers comes up and it is hot.

Did you answer all the questions?

Get well soon

Dear Steph,

Mum told me you broke your arm. She said you were bouncing on your bed and then you fell off. I hope it doesn't hurt too much. I broke my arm last year when I fell out of a tree. I got a green cast. What colour is yours? I miss you at school — it is boring sitting at a desk on my own. I hope you get well soon.

From Hannah

1 Who told Hannah about Steph's arm? Circle your answer.

(Hannah's mum) Steph's mum Steph

2 How did Steph break her arm?

She broke her arm by bouncing on beda

3 What colour was Hannah's cast?

Hannah's cast was gleen.

4 Why does Hannah want Steph to come back to school?

....

Did you answer all the questions?

A trip to the shop

Dad and Freddy went to the shop.

Freddy enjoys going to the shop because he gets to ride in the trolley.

They bought some <u>bread, some milk, some cheese and a box of cereal.</u>

Freddy's stomach rumbled and he said he was going to make a sandwich for lunch.

1 Who did Freddy go to the shop with?

Freddy went to the shop with his dad.

2 Why does Freddy like going to the shop?

He likes it because he get to ride in the trolley

3 How can you tell that Freddy was hungry?

Freddy's stomach rumbled and he said he was going to make a sandwich for lunch.

4 What kind of sandwich do you think Freddy will make? Think about what Dad and Freddy bought from the shop.

Freddy will make a cheese sandwich.

Did you answer all the questions?

No teacher

Today, our teacher was off ill and nobody came to teach us. Normally, we have maths on Monday mornings, but instead we played in the home corner. After break time, we usually have science, but today we painted pictures instead. Every day, we have one hour for lunch, but today nobody told us to go back to our lessons. We played outside until home time — it was fantastic!

1 Why didn't the children have a teacher today?

They didn't have a teacher because the teacher was off and ill.

2 What do the children usually study on Monday mornings?

Maths and Science

3 What does the word "fantastic" mean?

Fantastic mean a nice day, happy and fun

4 Why do you think the children didn't tell anyone that their teacher hadn't come?

They didn't tell anyone because it was a secret.

Did you answer all the questions?

The Enchanted Wood

"We've been exploring everywhere, Father!"
said Beth, pouring him out a big cup of tea.

"We've found a lovely wood," said Joe. "The trees
really seem to be talking to one another, Father."

"That must be the wood I've heard about this
afternoon," said Father. "It has a strange name, children."

"What is it called?" asked Joe.

"It's called the Enchanted Wood," said their father. "People don't go
there if they can help it. It's funny to hear things like this nowadays,
and I don't expect there is really anything strange about the wood.
But just be careful not to go too far into it, in case you get lost."

An extract from *The Enchanted Wood* by Enid Blyton.

1 What does "enchanted" mean? Circle your answer.

exciting   forbidden   scary   (magical)

2 What did the children find strange about the wood?

The children found out the was talking

3 Would you like to visit the Enchanted Wood? Why?

Yes! I would because it might have juicy fruits on it or the fruit might be sweet.

Did you answer all the questions?

     Year 2 — Targeted Comprehension

Amy Johnson

Amy Johnson was born in Hull in 1903. She began to take flying lessons when she was 25, and went on to become the first woman ever to fly alone from Britain to Australia. Amy flew to Australia in a Gipsy Moth plane, which she named Jason. During the Second World War, Amy helped the Royal Air Force by flying planes around the country. In 2016, giant sculptures of brightly coloured moths were hung on the walls of buildings around Hull to celebrate Amy's life.

1 How old was Amy when she started learning to fly?

Amy was 25 when she started learning to fly.

2 Why were moths chosen to celebrate Amy's life?

They celebrated Amy's life because she helped during world war second.

3 Is this text fiction or non-fiction? How can you tell?

Fiction

Did you answer all the questions?

Tim's Diary

Dear Diary,

Today, the weather was stormy so we couldn't go outside to play. We thought that the sun might come out this afternoon but it carried on raining. I really wanted to have a picnic in the garden but it was too wet, so Dad built a den in the kitchen to cheer me up. He used lots of blankets and pillows and it was very cosy. We ate a picnic inside the den. It was so yummy — we had jam sandwiches and crisps.

After that, we played a board game, and then we played in the den again until it was bath time.

Now I am tired. I will write to you again tomorrow.

1 How do you think Tim felt when he couldn't have a picnic outside? Tick two options.

☐ happy ☑ sad ☑ disappointed ☐ excited

2 Copy a word from the text that means the same as "tasty".

.....Yummy..

3 What do you think Tim did after writing in his diary? How can you tell?

.....Tim want to go bed because he is tired.....

....

Did you answer all the questions?

Plum

Don't be so glum,
plum.

Don't feel beaten.

You were made
to be eaten.

But don't you know
that deep within,

beneath your juicy flesh
and flimsy skin,

you bear a mystery,
you hold the key,

you have the making of
a whole new tree.

Tony Mitton

1 What does the word "glum" mean? Circle your answer.

excited   unhappy   silly   tasty

2 Which word in the poem rhymes with "eaten"?

Don't feel beaten. You were made to be eaten.

3 What is the mystery that the plum has inside it?

Inside a plum is a seed.

4 Copy down your favourite line. Explain why you like it.

You were made to be eaten. I like the line
because it is delicious.

Did you answer all the questions?

Making a bird feeder

How to make a bird feeder

1. Take a bagel and spread a layer of unsalted peanut butter over it. Make sure that it is quite thick.

2. Pour some birdseed onto a plate. Press the bagel into the birdseed until it is completely covered.

3. Thread a piece of string through the hole in the bagel.

4. Tie the string to the branch of a tree in the garden. Make sure it is tied tightly so it doesn't fall down.

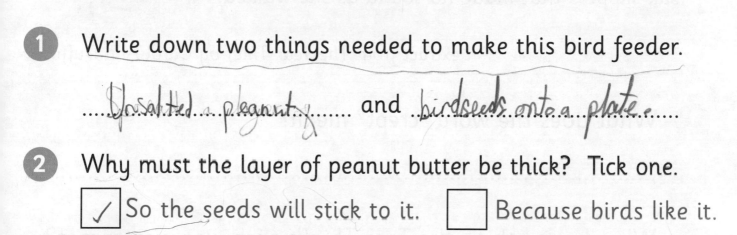

1 Write down two things needed to make this bird feeder.

..........Unsalted peannty.......... and ....birdseeds onto a plate......

2 Why must the layer of peanut butter be thick? Tick one.

[✓] So the seeds will stick to it.   [ ] Because birds like it.

3 Why is it important to tie the string tightly to the tree?

...So it doesn't fall down..................................

4 Would you like to make this bird feeder for your garden? Why or why not?

.....I would like to make a bird feeder in my.... garden because the birds will like me......

Did you answer all the questions?

The Tear Thief

Late one evening, the Tear Thief crept into town. The Tear Thief was invisible and carried a silvery waterproof sack on her back. Only if you happened to look into a puddle as she was passing could you see what the Tear Thief looked like, because a puddle was the one thing that showed her reflection. The Tear Thief had short, spiky white hair and big gray eyes. She wore a handkerchief dress and silk slippers that made no sound as she walked.

An extract from *The Tear Thief* by Carol Ann Duffy.

1 What does the word "crept" mean?

....

2 Why do you think the Tear Thief's sack was waterproof?

....

3 What is the only way to see the Tear Thief?

....

4 Is the Tear Thief big or small? How can you tell?

....

Did you answer all the questions?

The United Kingdom

UK stands for United Kingdom. There are four countries in the UK — Northern Ireland, Scotland, Wales and England. The UK's flag is called the Union Jack.

The capital of Northern Ireland is Belfast. The Irish Sea separates Northern Ireland from the rest of the UK.

Scotland's capital is Edinburgh. Scotland includes over seven hundred islands. Most of the islands don't have any people living on them.

Cardiff is the capital of Wales. Leeks and daffodils are symbols of Wales. People wear them on their clothes on St David's day.

England's capital city is London. England is the largest country in the UK and has the biggest population.

1 Why can't you walk from Northern Ireland to England?

....

2 Which UK country includes over seven hundred islands?

....

3 Write the names of two plants that are symbols of Wales.

.... and ....

4 Which country in the UK has the most people living there?

....

Did you answer all the questions? 🙁✓ 🙂✓ 😊✓

Our Solar System

There are eight planets in our Solar System. They all orbit the **Sun**.

The planets are written in their order from the Sun.

 Mercury is the smallest planet. It is closest to the Sun.

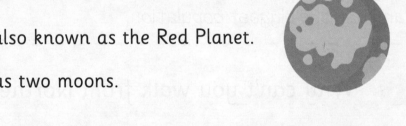 **Venus** is the hottest planet.

 **Earth** is the only planet in our Solar System

that is home to human beings.

Mars is also known as the Red Planet.

It has two moons.

 **Jupiter** is the biggest planet. It is a gas giant.

Saturn has rings. They are made

of small pieces of ice and rock.

 **Uranus** has twenty seven moons.

 **Neptune** is the planet furthest away from the Sun.

1 Write the number 1, 2, 3, 4 or 5 next to each planet to put them in the correct order from the Sun.

[4] Uranus   [3] Neptune   [2] Earth

[4] Jupiter   [1] Venus

2 Is Venus hotter or colder than Mars?

...Venuse is hotter than Mars....

3 Which planet do we live on?

...We live on the planet earth....

4 The Red Planet is another name for which planet?

...The Red plant is Mars....

5 Why is "giant" a good word to describe Jupiter?

...good....

6 What are Saturn's rings made of?

...They are made of small pieces of ice and rock....

Did you answer all the questions? 😟✓ 🙂✓ 😊✓

On the farm

Farms are always really busy, and this one is no exception. Andy has already milked the cow, and he's about to start digging up the cabbages. He's wearing black boots and blue overalls so that his clothes don't get too muddy. Josh's hat is orange. He's picking strawberries and putting them carefully into a yellow bowl. He is only picking big, juicy, red ones — the smaller green ones aren't ripe yet. Susan is wearing purple overalls with a green pocket. She is feeding the animals. Rachel has got red boots on so that she doesn't get dirty in the mud. She's going to collect eggs from the hens and put them in her blue basket. What a busy morning!

1 Put a tick in each row to show which child is wearing which item of clothing.

	Andy	Josh	Susan	Rachel
red boots				✓
blue overalls	✓			
orange hat	✓	✓		
purple overalls			✓	

2 What is Andy going to do next?

...Andy...is...going...to...dig...the...cabbages...

3 Why do you think Josh is putting the strawberries into the bowl carefully?

...I...think...because...

4 What is Susan doing?

......

5 Why are Susan and Andy wearing overalls?

......

6 Why has Rachel brought a basket?

......

Did you answer all the questions? 😟✓ 🙂✓ 😊✓

Year 2 — Targeted Comprehension

Sports

To stay healthy, it's important to do plenty of exercise.

There are lots of different sports that you can do.

 Football uses a round ball. There are eleven players on a team, including a goalkeeper. Only the goalkeeper is allowed to touch the ball with their hands.

 Badminton is played by two people competing against each other, or by two teams of two. You use a racquet to hit a shuttlecock (a small ball with feathers attached) over a net. The shuttlecock isn't allowed to hit the ground.

 Table tennis is also known as ping pong. It can be played with two or four players. A small red and black bat is used to hit a white or orange ball over a net on a table. The ball must bounce at least once on the other side of the table before it is hit back.

 Basketball uses a big, round ball. There are five players on a team. You have to bounce the ball when you run with it. Players try to score by throwing the ball into a round net raised off the ground.

 Judo is a martial art — a sport that involves self-defence. Two people compete against each other. They must use special moves to try to pin each other to the ground.

1 Why is it important to do exercise?

It is important to do exercise to stay healthy.

2 In football, how many people on each team are allowed to pick up the ball?

11 players are allowed in each team.

3 Table tennis uses a shuttlecock. Is this true or false?

False!

4 Judo is a martial art. Explain what this means.

This means it involves self-defence.

5 Which sport is played by the largest team?

Football is played by the largest team.

6 Which do you think would be the hardest sport? Why?

Judo because you must use special moves to try to pin each other to the ground.

7 Do you like to play sports? Which one is your favourite?

Yes! I like to play sports and my favourite sport is badminton.

Did you answer all the questions? 😞 🙂 😊

Habitats

A habitat is a place where a plant or animal lives. There are lots of different habitats. Different kinds of animals and plants live in each one.

Desert

A desert habitat is somewhere that doesn't get a lot of rain. There aren't many plants and it is difficult for animals to live there. Some desert habitats can get very hot, but others are very cold. One of the largest deserts in the world is the Sahara in Africa.

Tropical Rainforest

Tropical rainforest habitats are found near to the Equator. They are really hot and they also get a lot of rain. The biggest tropical rainforest in the world is the Amazon. Rainforest trees are very tall — some reach over 45 metres. Huge numbers of insects, birds and other animals live in tropical rainforest habitats.

Ocean

Oceans are very large areas of salt water. They can be warm or cold. The Pacific Ocean is the biggest ocean in the world. Ocean habitats are home to dolphins, corals, starfish, turtles and many other living things.

Urban

An urban area is somewhere that has been built on by humans — like a town or city. Lots of people live in urban habitats, but animals like rats and pigeons have learnt how to live in them too.

1 Why do you think it is difficult for animals to live in desert habitats?

....

2 What is the biggest tropical rainforest in the world?

....

3 Give one difference between a desert and a rainforest.

....

4 What is an ocean?

....

5 Name two animals that live in an ocean habitat.

.... and ....

6 What type of habitat is the city of London?

....

7 Can you think of another wild animal that has learnt to live in an urban habitat?

....

Did you answer all the questions?

Year 2 — Targeted Comprehension

Flat Stanley

Breakfast was ready.

"I will go wake the boys," Mrs. Lambchop said to her husband, George Lambchop. Just then their younger son, Arthur, called from the bedroom he shared with his brother, Stanley.

"Hey! Come and look! Hey!"

Mr. and Mrs. Lambchop were both very much in favor of politeness and careful speech. "Hay is for horses, Arthur, not people," Mr. Lambchop said as they entered the bedroom. "Try to remember that."

"Excuse me," Arthur said. "But look!"

He pointed to Stanley's bed. Across it lay the enormous bulletin board that Mr. Lambchop had given the boys a Christmas ago so that they could pin up pictures and messages and maps. It had fallen, during the night, on top of Stanley.

But Stanley was not hurt. In fact, he would still have been sleeping if he had not been woken by his brother's shout.

"What's going on here?" he called out cheerfully from beneath the enormous board.

Mr. and Mrs. Lambchop hurried to lift it from the bed.

"Heavens!" said Mrs. Lambchop.

"Gosh!" said Arthur. "Stanley's flat!"

"As a pancake," said Mr. Lambchop.

An extract from *Flat Stanley* by Jeff Brown.

1 At what time of day is the text set? How do you know?

....

2 Is Stanley older or younger than Arthur?

....

3 Why do you think the author uses exclamation marks when Arthur says "Hey! Come and look! Hey!"?

....

4 Why does Mr. Lambchop tell Arthur "Hay is for horses"?

....

....

5 What woke Stanley up?

....

6 Copy a word from the text that shows Stanley isn't worried about being under the board.

....

Did you answer all the questions?

Animals

Animals can be put into groups based on what they eat. **Herbivores** eat plants.
Carnivores eat meat (other animals). **Omnivores** eat both plants and meat.

piranha	I'm a fish that lives in rivers in South America. I'm an omnivore — I eat seeds and plants as well as other fish.
frog	I'm an amphibian. I lay my eggs in water and I eat insects. I have strong legs for jumping, but I didn't have them when I was born. I started life as a tadpole then grew into a frog.
snake	I'm a reptile. I don't have any legs, and I usually eat eggs and mice. I swallow my food whole without chewing it.
bat	I'm a mammal that can fly. I'm nocturnal — I sleep during the day. I like to sleep hanging upside down. I eat insects. My big ears help me to find them in the dark.
ostrich	I'm a bird but I can't fly. I live in Africa. I am very big, and have long, strong legs. I'm an omnivore — I eat berries, roots, lizards and insects.
zebra	I'm a mammal — I make milk for my babies. I live in Africa and I eat grass. I'm a herbivore. Every zebra in the world is unique because each zebra's stripes are a little bit different.

1 Which group of animals only eats plants?

...... Herbivores ....

2 Why do frogs have strong legs?

...... Frogs have strong legs for jumping ....

3 How can you tell that snakes are carnivores?

Snakes usually eat eggs and mice. ....

4 Why do bats need to have very good hearing?

...... Bats have big ears to help them find insects ...

5 Can all birds fly? Explain how you know this from the text.

....

6 What does the word "unique" mean?

....

7 Give one example of a mammal from the text.
What makes an animal a mammal?

....

....

Did you answer all the questions?

Slippers at school?

Primary school encourages pupils to wear slippers in class

Children at an East Midlands primary school are being encouraged to wear slippers in class.

Findern primary in Derby introduced the idea after one of the teachers came across research that found the relaxed approach to footwear improved academic results. […]

Michelle Hall, Findern's deputy head, said: "It was suggested by one of the teachers after seeing some research that wearing slippers can improve children's grades. We pitched the idea to the pupils and they were very excited. It's been a huge success so far and even staff are wearing slippers in the classroom too.

"Our pupils have always been well behaved but we've noticed some changes. There is less stomping around and children are calmer and more relaxed. They love it."

Maisie Futcher, a pupil, thought it was "a great idea". The 10-year-old added: "I love wearing my slippers at home, so it's nice being able to wear them at school. It makes me feel relaxed and helps me to learn."

An abridged article from *www.theguardian.com*

1 Why do the teachers want the children to wear slippers?
Tick one.

☐ Because the children move more quietly in slippers.

☐ Because research showed that it could improve their grades.

☐ Because the children kept getting cold feet in the classroom.

2 The teachers "pitched the idea" to the pupils.
What do you think this means?

....

3 Copy the sentence that describes what has changed at the school since slippers were allowed.

....

....

4 How do the children in the article feel about wearing slippers to school?

....

5 Would you like to wear slippers at school? Why or why not?

....

....

Did you answer all the questions?

Year 2 — Targeted Comprehension

The Selfish Giant

Every afternoon, the children played in the Giant's garden.

It was a large, lovely garden, with soft, green grass and beautiful flowers. The trees were full of birds that sang sweetly.

One day, the Giant came back. He had been away for many years. When he arrived, he saw the children playing in the garden.

"What are you doing?" he shouted furiously, and the children ran away.

"This is my garden," said the Giant. "I won't let anyone but me play here." He built a high wall around the garden and put up a sign.

KEEP OUT!

He was a very selfish Giant.

The poor children had nowhere to play. They stared up at the wall and talked about the beautiful garden inside.

Then spring came and flowers bloomed all over the country. Only in the garden of the Selfish Giant it was still winter. The birds didn't want to sing in the garden as there were no children, and the trees forgot to blossom.

"I don't understand why spring hasn't come," said the Selfish Giant, as he looked out at his cold, white garden. "I hope there will be a change in the weather."

But spring never came, and neither did summer or autumn.

One morning, the Giant heard some lovely music. It was a small bird singing outside his window. Then the snow stopped falling and the wind stopped roaring. "I think spring has finally come," said the Giant as he peered out of the window.

What did he see?

He saw a wonderful sight. The children had crept into the garden and they were sitting in the branches of the trees. The trees were so glad to have the children back that they had covered themselves with blossom. Birds were twittering with delight, and the flowers were in full bloom.

An adapted version of *The Selfish Giant* by Oscar Wilde.

1 Find and copy two adjectives which describe the grass in the Giant's garden.

.... and ....

2 What do you think "furiously" means?

....

3 Write down a word to describe how the children felt when they left the garden. Explain your answer.

....

....

4 Why is the Giant described as "selfish"?

....

5 What does this story teach us about being selfish?

....

....

6 Did you like this story? Why or why not?

....

....

Did you answer all the questions?

　　　　　　　　　Year 2 — Targeted Comprehension

The Monkeys and the Crocodile

Five little monkeys
Swinging from a tree;
Teasing Uncle Crocodile,
Merry as can be.
Swinging high, swinging low,
Swinging left and right:
"Dear Uncle Crocodile,
Come and take a bite!"

Five little monkeys
Swinging in the air;
Heads up, tails up,
Little do they care.
Swinging up, swinging down,
Swinging far and near:
"Poor Uncle Crocodile,
Aren't you hungry, dear?"

Four little monkeys
Sitting in a tree;
Heads down, tails down,
Dreary as can be.
Weeping loud, weeping low,
Crying to each other:
"Wicked Uncle Crocodile,
To gobble up our brother!"

by Laura Richards